Estimation: Grade 1

Table of Contents

Introduction

Estimation skills are an important tool in school and in real-life situations. The ability to make educated guesses and logical choices is the result of practice in estimation. Students should be able to make sensible estimates and then use tools to check their estimates for accuracy. Practicing their estimating skills enables students to make increasingly better estimates. When students estimate well, it becomes clear when an answer is incorrect and needs to be rechecked. Throughout daily life, we all regularly make choices using estimation skills. The more practiced we are, the fewer mistakes we will make.

Estimation is meant as a supplementary workbook to help students practice and increase their estimating abilities. The units are Concepts, Computation, Problem Solving, and Enrichment. Students can practice estimating measurement of length, weight, capacity, temperature, time, and money. They guess and check computation and work with rounding numbers, choosing reasonable answers, and problem-solving strategies. The Enrichment unit gives students the opportunity to use their imagination and what they have learned in real-life situations.

Assessments have been provided as a tool to gauge student progress. There is a general assessment and an assessment for each of the first three units.

A Letter to Parents is included on page 2. Send it home with the students and encourage them to share it with their parents.

Dear Parent:

During this school year, our class will be practicing skills in estimation. Strong estimation skills are important to success in mathematics, as well as in other schoolwork. When you think of the many times each day that you use estimation to make choices and decisions, it becomes clear how useful it is to have strong estimation skills.

There are things that you can do at home to help your child practice his or her estimation skills. Here are some suggestions:

- If your child brings home a worksheet, provide a quiet place to work.
- Go over directions together, and encourage your child to do his or her best.
- Check the lesson when it is complete, noting problems as well as improvements.
- Play games with estimation at home. Ask questions such as "How long do you think it will take?," "How far do you think it is?," or "How much do you think that will cost?"
- Share your own estimations with your child, and explain how you make them.
- When possible, check to see if your estimations were close to the actual measurements of time, length, height, or cost.

Above all, enjoy the time you spend estimating with your child. You both can have fun, and your child will feel your support. You will be able to watch your child's estimation skills improve.

Sincerely,

What Do You Think?

 Circle the one that is the heaviest.

1.

 Circle the one that has the most milk.

2.

 Circle the one that is the warmest.

3.

 Circle the one that would take the most time.

4.

planting a tree   building a tower   mailing a letter

Go on to the next page.

What Do You Think?, p. 2

 How far? Guess, then check with a centimeter ruler or an inch ruler.

5.

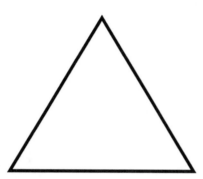

Guess: ____ centimeters
Check: ____ centimeters

6.

Guess: ____ inches
Check: ____ inches

 Write <, >, or =. Then, count to check your answer. Write the amount on the tag.

7.

 Circle the ones that are divided evenly.

8. a.    **b.**    **c.**    **d.**

Concepts

 Circle the one that is lighter.

1.

 How long is it? Guess, then measure with an inch ruler to check.

2.

Guess: ____ inch(es)
Check: ____ inch(es)

3.

Guess: ____ inches
Check: ____ inches

 Which will take the most time? Circle it.

4.

mowing the lawn   feeding the dog   eating a snack

 Solve this problem.

5. Tom has a 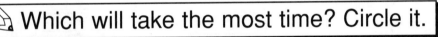. Ann has a _____.
Who would use more lengths to measure a room?
Circle the name.   Tom   Ann

Name _____ Date _____

Clipping Right Along

Find these objects in your classroom.
About how many ⬭ long is each one?
Estimate. Then, use ⬭ to measure.

	Objects	Estimate	Measurement
1.	ERASER	about _____ ⬭	about _____ ⬭
2.	(tissue box)	about _____ ⬭	about _____ ⬭
3.	(book)	about _____ ⬭	about _____ ⬭
4.	(desk)	about _____ ⬭	about _____ ⬭

Solve this problem.

5. Rita has a 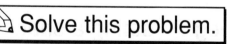. Max has a ⬭.
Who would use more lengths to measure a desk?
Circle the name. Tell why.   Rita   Max

Name _____ Date _____

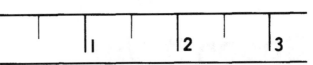

Leaf Length

 About how long is each leaf?

1.

about _____ inches

2.

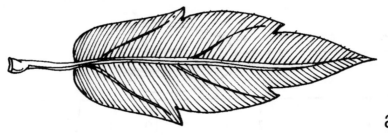

about _____ inches

3.

about _____ inches

4.

about _____ inches

Spoon It Up!

 About how long is each object?

1.   about _____ cm

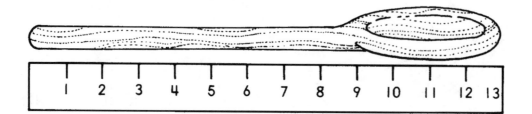

2.   about _____ cm

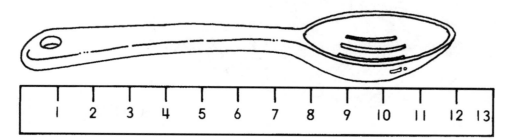

3.   about _____ cm

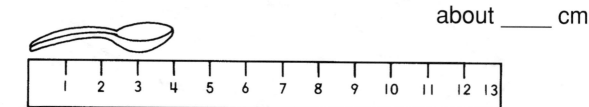

4.   about _____ cm

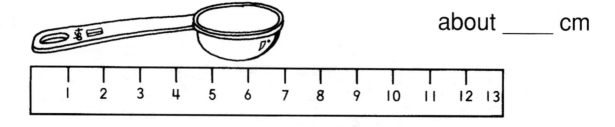

How Long Does It Look?

 Write the number of centimeters.

1.

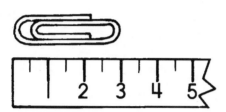

_____ cm

2.

_____ cm

 About how long is each object?

3.

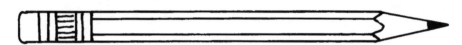

about _____ cm

4.

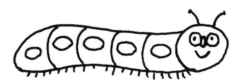

about _____ cm

5.

about _____ cm

"Weight" for Me!

 Circle the object in each pair that is heavier.

1.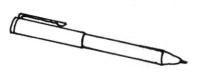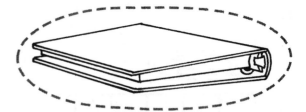

2.

3.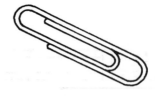

4.

 Solve this problem.

5. Anita puts these objects on a balance. Circle the heaviest object.

cup   pan   block

Pour It On!

 Circle the better estimate.

1.

more than 1 quart
less than 1 quart

2.

more than 1 cup
less than 1 cup

 Color the cups to show more.

3.

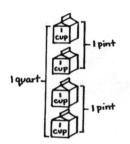

Pint

4.

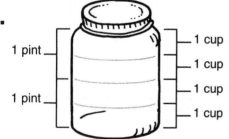

Quart

 Circle the best answer.

5. Marta has 1 quart of juice.
How many cups can she fill?

3   2   4

How Long?

| Which takes more time to complete? Circle it. |

1.

2.

3.

| Solve this problem. Circle the correct answer. |

4. Manny has these puzzles. Which takes the most time?

PUZZLE **50**   PUZZLE **100**   PUZZLE **75**

Say "When"!

| Circle in green what happened first. |
| Circle in red what happened last. |

1.

2.

3.

 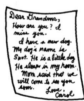 

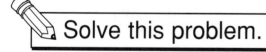 Solve this problem.

4. Rob and Ann sell lemonade. Write numbers to tell the order these events happened.

_____   _____   _____   _____

Name _____   Date _____

Heating Up

 Circle the one in each pair that is hot.

1.

2.

3.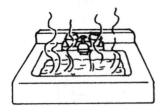

4.

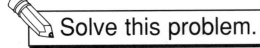 Solve this problem.

5. Ellen measures the temperature of these objects.
Circle the one that shows the hottest temperature.

Unit 1: Concepts: Degrees Fahrenheit

Estimation 1, SV 2921-1

Hot and Cold

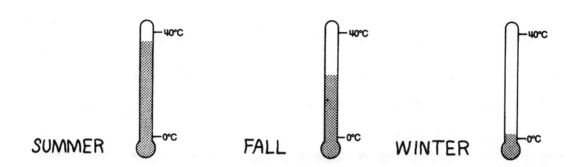

SUMMER   FALL   WINTER

What do you think the temperature is? Color the thermometer to show the temperature.

1.

2.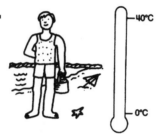

3.

4.

5.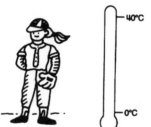

6.

7. What is the temperature now?
Color it on the thermometer.

Counting Coins

Look at the coins. Guess if the amount in the first box is more, less, or the same as the amount in the second box. Write <, >, or =. Then, count the coins to check your answer.

1.

_____   _____

2.

_____   _____

3.

_____   _____

4.

_____   _____

Computation

 Guess and check.

1. How many square
centimeters?

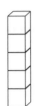

Guess: ____ sq cm
Check: ____ sq cm

2. How many cubes in
the shape?

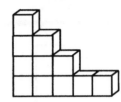

Guess: ____ cubes
Check: ____ cubes

 Round up or down to the nearest 10.
Circle the best answer.

3. 59   60   55   50   **4.** 12   10   15   20

 Use front-end estimation to add.

5.	43 →	40	**6.**	23 →		**7.**	46 →	
	+ 21 →	+ 20		+ 15 →			+ 11 →	

 You have 50¢. Circle the fruits you could buy.

8.

Name _____   Date _____

How Far Around?

Guess how many inches are around each shape.
Then, use an inch ruler to measure each side.
Add the length of each side to find the total length
around the shape.

1.

Guess: _____   Check: _____

2.

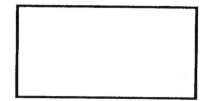

Guess: _____   Check: _____

3.

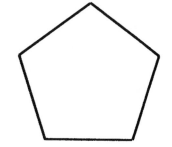

Guess: _____   Check: _____

4.

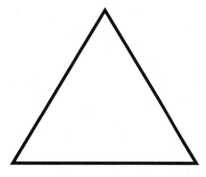

Guess: _____   Check: _____

Counting Squares

1 square centimeter

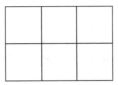

6 square centimeters

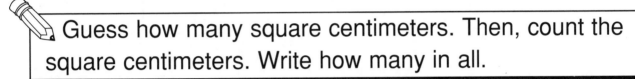

Guess how many square centimeters. Then, count the square centimeters. Write how many in all.

1.

Guess: ___   Check: ___

2.

Guess: ___   Check: ___

3.

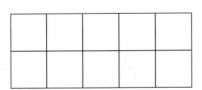

Guess: ___   Check: ___

4.

Guess: ___   Check: ___

5.

Guess: ___   Check: ___

6.

Guess: ___   Check: ___

Building Blocks

Guess the number of centimeter cubes in each shape.
Then, count the cubes to check your answer.

1.

Guess: ___   Check: ___

2.

Guess: ___   Check: ___

3.

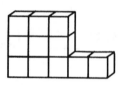

Guess: ___   Check: ___

4.

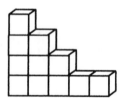

Guess: ___   Check: ___

5.

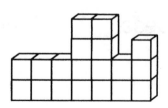

Guess: ___   Check: ___

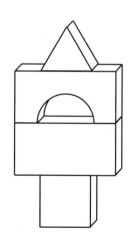

Counting Sheep

 Circle the answer that makes sense.

1.   5
   + 1

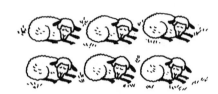

more than 5
less than 5
equal to 5

2.   7
   − 3

more than 7
less than 7
equal to 7

3.   5
   + 0

more than 5
less than 5
equal to 5

4.   3
   − 0

more than 3
less than 3
equal to 3

5.   4
   + 4

more than 4
less than 4
equal to 4

Adding It Up

Estimate the sums by adding the numbers in the tens place.

Example:

$$
\begin{array}{r}
\underline{4}2 \\
+\ \underline{3}1 \\
\hline
?
\end{array}
\longrightarrow
\begin{array}{r}
40 \\
+\ 30 \\
\hline
70
\end{array}
$$

1. $\begin{array}{r} 52 \\ +\ 16 \\ \hline \end{array} \longrightarrow +\ \underline{\quad}$

2. $\begin{array}{r} 33 \\ +\ 12 \\ \hline \end{array} \longrightarrow +\ \underline{\quad}$

3. $\begin{array}{r} 45 \\ +\ 61 \\ \hline \end{array} \longrightarrow +\ \underline{\quad}$

4. $\begin{array}{r} 27 \\ +\ 48 \\ \hline \end{array} \longrightarrow +\ \underline{\quad}$

5. $\begin{array}{r} 63 \\ +\ 41 \\ \hline \end{array} \longrightarrow +\ \underline{\quad}$

6. $\begin{array}{r} 71 \\ +\ 24 \\ \hline \end{array} \longrightarrow +\ \underline{\quad}$

7. $\begin{array}{r} 33 \\ +\ 25 \\ \hline \end{array} \longrightarrow +\ \underline{\quad}$

8. $\begin{array}{r} 15 \\ +\ 43 \\ \hline \end{array} \longrightarrow +\ \underline{\quad}$

9. $\begin{array}{r} 42 \\ +\ 57 \\ \hline \end{array} \longrightarrow +\ \underline{\quad}$

Name _____ Date _____

Toy Store-y

  Look at each group of toys. Circle the amount that you think they would cost. Then, use a (calculator) to check your answer.

TOYS	ESTIMATE (about)	EXACT SUM
1. Bear 35¢ Ball 10¢ Airplane 40¢	75¢ 85¢ 45¢	
2. Airplane 30¢ Car 25¢ Baseball 33¢	88¢ 50¢ 32¢	
3. Jump rope 20¢ Dinosaur 15¢ Football 55¢	75¢ 45¢ 90¢	

Food Shopping

 Write how much you think each item would cost.
Hint: Write amounts more than 1 dollar like this: $1.20.
Write amounts less than one dollar like this: 35¢.

soup

cost: _____

bread

cost: _____

muffin

cost: _____

quart of milk

cost: _____

pack of gum

cost: _____

peach

cost: _____

steak

cost: _____

box of cereal

cost: _____

box of raisins

cost: _____

Write the amount you would need to buy the foods
on each list. Round up to the nearest dollar.

1. milk
steak
cereal
$_____

2. gum
peach
muffin
$_____

3. raisins
soup
bread
$_____

4. milk
cereal
peach
$_____

Bring this paper to a food store. Find the cost of each food.
How close were your guesses?

Round Up (and Down!)

When rounding numbers, look at the number in the ones place. Is it more than 5, less than 5, or equal to 5?

If it is equal to 5 or more than 5, round up.   65 → 70
If it is less than 5, round down.   64 → 60

Circle the best answer to round to the nearest 10.

1. 47   60   50   40   **2.** 5   10   0   15

3. 24   20   25   30   **4.** 3   0   10   5

5. 13   20   10   0   **6.** 66   70   65   60

Round each number to the nearest 10. Circle <u>Up</u> or <u>Down</u>. Then, write your answer.

7. 38   Up Down ____   **8.** 77   Up Down ____

9. 27   Up Down ____   **10.** 35   Up Down ____

11. 82   Up Down ____   **12.** 52   Up Down ____

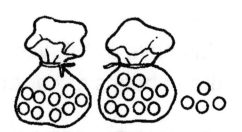

Mark's Market

Look at the sign for Mark's Market. Estimate to answer the questions about the sign. You may use a  (calculator) to add.

[Hint: lb = pound and ea = each.]

1. You have $1.00. Can you buy 1 pound of green beans?

_____

2. Could you buy 2 pounds of carrots with $2.00?

_____

3. You have $2.00. Can you buy 2 red peppers?

_____

4. You have $0.50. Do you need more or less money to buy 1 pound of navy beans?

_____

5. Can you buy 1 pound of tomatoes with $0.75?

_____

6. You have $1.00. Which vegetable can you buy more of, green beans or carrots?

_____

Problem Solving

 Circle the triangle that is divided into equal parts.

1.

 Use the graph to answer the questions.

2. Did they sell more 🌸 or 🥕 seeds?

_____

3. Did they sell fewer 🦆 or 🌱 seeds?

_____

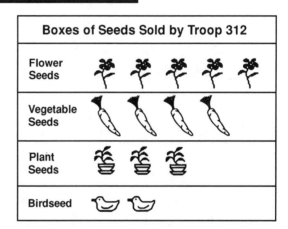

 Add the shapes you need to make a ▢ .

4.

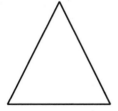

 Do you need to add or subtract? Circle one.

5. You see 4 boys swimming in a pond. You see 3 girls swimming in the pond. How many children do you see?

Add   Subtract

Even It Out

Guess the number that will make the scale balance.
Add to check your answer.

1.

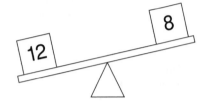

2   4   6

2.

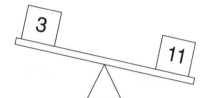

6   7   8

3.

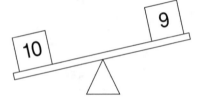

0   1   2

4.

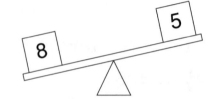

3   4   5

5.

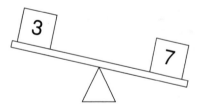

4   5   6

6.

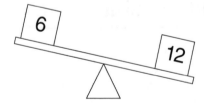

4   5   6

7.

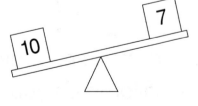

2   3   4

8.

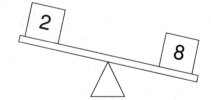

6   7   8

Plenty of Parts

 Does the shape have equal parts? Circle <u>yes</u> or <u>no</u>.

1.

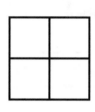

yes   no

2.

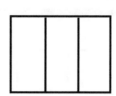

yes   no

3.

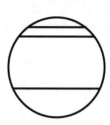

yes   no

4.

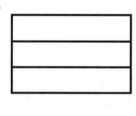

yes   no

5.

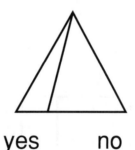

yes   no

6.

yes   no

 Color the shapes with equal parts.

7.

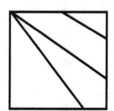

8.

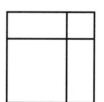 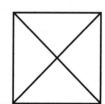

9.

10.

Name _____ Date _____

Fraction Fun

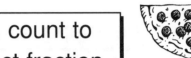

✏️ Guess what part is shaded. Then, count to check your answer. Circle the correct fraction.

1.

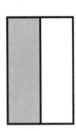

$\frac{1}{2}$ $\frac{1}{3}$ $\frac{1}{4}$

2.

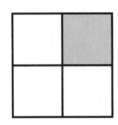

$\frac{1}{2}$ $\frac{1}{3}$ $\frac{1}{4}$

3.

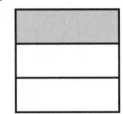

$\frac{1}{2}$ $\frac{1}{3}$ $\frac{1}{4}$

4.

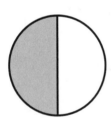

$\frac{1}{2}$ $\frac{1}{3}$ $\frac{1}{4}$

5.

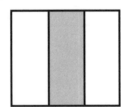

$\frac{1}{2}$ $\frac{1}{3}$ $\frac{1}{4}$

6.

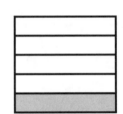

$\frac{1}{5}$ $\frac{1}{3}$ $\frac{1}{4}$

7.

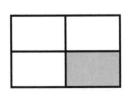

$\frac{1}{2}$ $\frac{1}{3}$ $\frac{1}{4}$

8.

$\frac{1}{5}$ $\frac{1}{3}$ $\frac{1}{4}$

9.

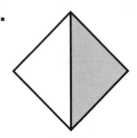

$\frac{1}{2}$ $\frac{1}{3}$ $\frac{1}{4}$

Pizza Pieces

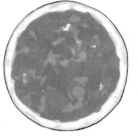

Think about sharing a pizza.
Solve the problems.

1. You want to give 3 children equal parts.
How could you cut the pizza? Circle it.

2. You want to give 4 children equal parts.
How could you cut the pizza? Circle it.

3. You want to give 2 children equal parts.
How could you cut the pizza? Circle it.

 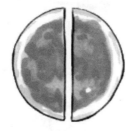  

Bread and Butter

Show another way to cut the food into the same number of equal parts. Make the pieces the same size.

Name _____ Date _____

Shape Up!

Draw a different shape.
Use the same number of square centimeters.

1.

2.

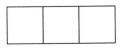

3.

4.

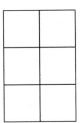

Name _____ Date _____

It Figures

 Color each shape that you think will stack.

1.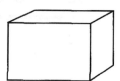

 Color each shape that you think will roll.

2.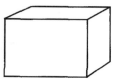

 Color each shape that you think will slide.

3.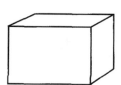

 Use solid shapes to check your answers.

4. Draw each shape that will stack.

5. Draw each shape that will roll.

6. Draw each shape that will slide.

Look-Alikes

Add the shape you need to make a ▭ .

1. ▢

Add the shape you need to make a ◇ .

2.  ◁

Add the shape you need to make a ◯ .

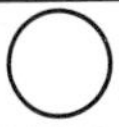

3.  ◗

Add the shape you need to make a ▢ .

4. 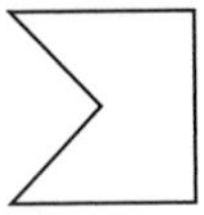 ⊐

Now, take away the shape you need to make a � . Color it blue.

5. ▢

Take away the shapes you need to make a ▭ . Color them red.

6. 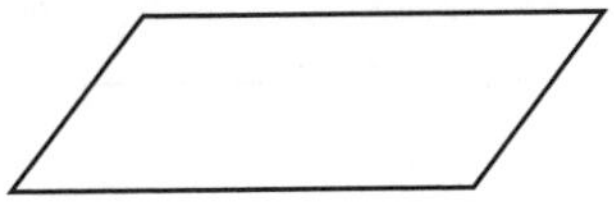 ▱

Name _____ Date _____

At the Pond

Darcy made a graph to show how many animals she saw at the pond.

She drew for 2 animals.

How Many Animals?

Kind of animal	Number of animals
snake 🐍	🐚 🐚 🐚
frog 🐸	🐚 🐚 🐚 🐚
lizard 🦎	🐚 🐚
turtle 🐢	🐚 🐚 🐚 🐚 🐚

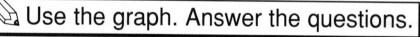

Use the graph. Answer the questions.

1. Are there more or more ? _____

2. Are there more or more ? _____

3. How many more than ? _____

4. How many more than ? _____

House of Shapes

 Guess how many of each shape make the picture. Then, count the shapes. Complete the graph.

Guess

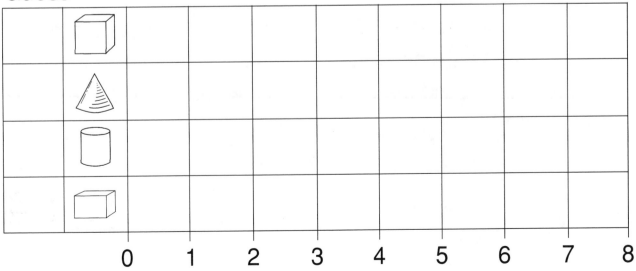

0   1   2   3   4   5   6   7   8

Add or Subtract?

 | Would you add or subtract? Circle the sign.

1. You have 3 books. You get 2 more. How many are there in all?

+   −

2. You see 5 bikes. 4 roll away. How many are left?

+   −

3. You have 6 toys. You give 2 away. How many are left?

+   −

4. You see 2 red cars. You see 3 blue cars. How many do you see in all?

+   −

5. You see 4 red balloons. You see 1 blue balloon. How many balloons do you see?

+   −

6. You see 7 blue and green kites. 3 kites are green. How many kites are blue?

+   −

Name _____ Date _____

Work It Out

 Solve.

1. Mark has a pencil box that is 8 inches long. His pencil is 7 inches long. Will his pencil fit in the box? Circle <u>yes</u> or <u>no</u>.

yes   no

2. Fran wants the biggest jar of paint she can buy. Circle the paint Fran will buy.

3. Mark has a hamster. Darla has a kitten. Circle the animal that weighs more.

4. Isa left her crayons outside. Her crayons melted. What was the temperature? Circle the picture to show what the temperature was.

Unit 3: Problem Solving: Word Problems
Estimation 1, SV 2921-1

Name _____ Date _____

Soccer Time

Soccer practice starts at 4:30. How long will
it take you to get ready? How long does it
take you to get to the field from your house?
Draw hands on the clocks to show a time
schedule. Draw or write what you do at each time.

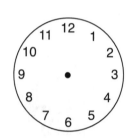

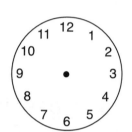

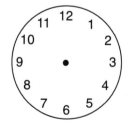

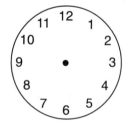

Bed Time

What must you do before going to bed each night?
How long do you think each activity takes?

Activity	Time

Now, think about the time you should be in
bed. Using the above table, what time should
you start to get ready for bed?

_____

- -

My bedtime is _____ .

_____

- -

I should start to get ready for bed at _____ .

What Could You Do?

Look at the thermometer. Draw or write about
several activities that you could do outside if
this was the temperature.

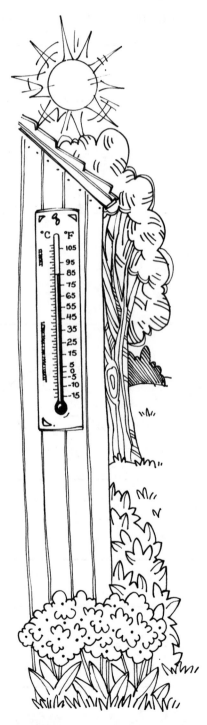

Juice Jug

You have a jug of juice. There are 8 of you to share it. How can you use a cup to make sure everyone gets the same amount of juice?

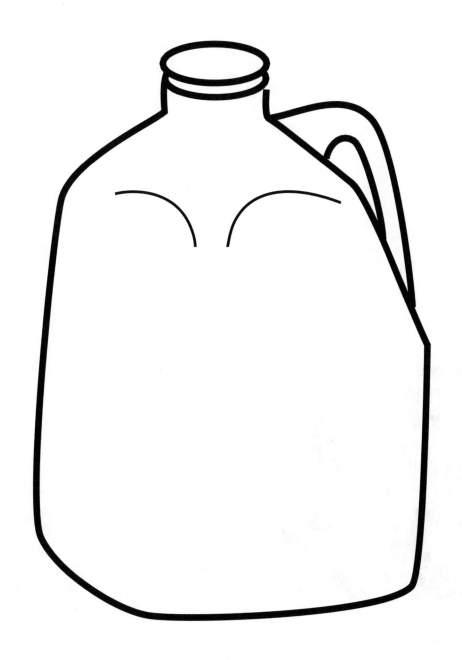

Name _____ Date _____

Sky High

How can you find out how tall an apartment building is without using a ruler or a tape measure? Write your ideas.

Name _____ Date _____

Let's Go Shopping!

Get a handful of coins. What do you think you could buy?
Count the coins. Were you right? Try different groups of
toys and flowers.

Room to Draw

Draw the outline of your bedroom. Show where your furniture is. Be sure to show where the door and windows are. Think about how big or small each thing is.

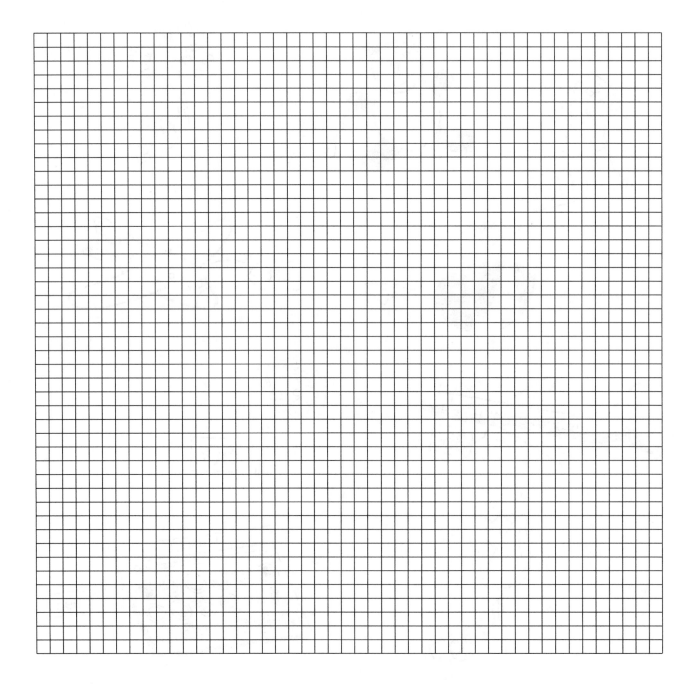

Pattern Play

Get a handful of color shape blocks.
See how many patterns you can
make. Draw and color the patterns
below. Get a friend to find the block
that comes next in each pattern.

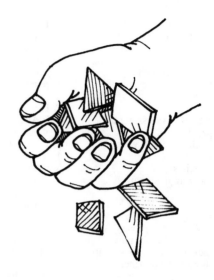

Estimation: Grade 1

Answer Key

Pp. 3–4 General Assessment
1. chicken
2. gallon
3. boiling pot
4. planting a tree
5–6. Guesses will vary.
5. 15 cm around
6. 8 inches around
7. =; 30 cents each
8. a, b, d

P. 5 Unit 1 Assessment
1. peach
2–3. Guesses will vary.
2. 1 inch
3. 3 inches
4. mowing the lawn
5. Tom

P. 6
1–4. Answers will vary.
5. Max would use more lengths because a paper clip is shorter than a pencil.

P. 7
1. about 3 inches
2. about 4 inches
3. about 5 inches
4. about 6 inches

P. 8
1. about 13 cm
2. about 12 cm
3. about 4 cm
4. about 7 cm

P. 9
1. 3 cm
2. 2 cm
3. about 12 cm
4. about 6 cm
5. about 8 cm

P. 10
1. notebook
2. book
3. paste
4. crayons
5. pan is heaviest

P. 11
1. less than 1 quart
2. more than 1 cup
3. color more than 2 cups
4. color more than 1 cup
5. 4 cups

P. 12
1. boy on right
2. man on left
3. woman on right
4. 100-piece puzzle

P. 13
1. Green: full glass; Red: empty glass
2. Green: 1st pencil; Red, 3rd pencil

3. Green: blank paper; Red: finished letter
4. 1, 4, 3, 2

P. 14
1. teapot
2. hamburger
3. sink
4. pot
5. center; hot soup

P. 15
2–6; Answers will vary.
2. about 30°C
3. about 0°C
4. about 15°C
5. about 20°C
6. about 5°C
7. Check for reasonable response.

P. 16
1. 35¢ < 63¢
2. 44¢ > 35¢
3. 46¢ < 56¢
4. 40¢ = 40¢

P. 17 Unit 2 Assessment
1–2. Guesses will vary.
1. 5 sq cm
2. 11 cubes
3. 60
4. 10
5. 60
6. 20 + 10 = 30
7. 40 + 10 = 50
8. banana and orange or apple

P. 18
1. 4 inches
2. 6 inches
3. 5 inches
4. 6 inches

P. 19
1. 2 square centimeters
2. 4 square centimeters
3. 10 square centimeters
4. 8 square centimeters
5. 3 square centimeters
6. 4 square centimeters

P. 20
1. 3 cubes
2. 10 cubes
3. 11 cubes
4. 11 cubes
5. 19 cubes

P. 21
1. more than 5
2. less than 7
3. equal to 5
4. equal to 3
5. more than 4

P. 22
1. 50 + 10 = 60
2. 30 + 10 = 40

3. 40 + 60 = 100
4. 20 + 40 = 60
5. 60 + 40 = 100
6. 70 + 20 = 90
7. 30 + 20 = 50
8. 10 + 40 = 50
9. 40 + 50 = 90

P. 23
Estimates may vary.
1. 85¢
2. 88¢
3. 90¢

P. 24
Answers will vary. Check for reasonable responses.

P. 25
1. 50
2. 10
3. 20
4. 0
5. 10
6. 70
7. Up; 40
8. Up; 80
9. Up; 30
10. Up; 40
11. Down; 80
12. Down; 50

P. 26
1. no
2. yes
3. yes
4. less
5. yes
6. carrots

P. 27 Unit 3 Assessment
1. center triangle
2. flower seeds
3. birdseed
4. Students add 2 triangles.
5. Add

P. 28
1. 4
2. 8
3. 1
4. 3
5. 4
6. 6
7. 3
8. 6

P. 29
1. yes
2. yes
3. no
4. yes
5. no
6. yes
7–10. Check students' work.
7. right square
8. right square
9. left circle
10. left triangle

P. 30
1. 1/2
2. 1/4
3. 1/3
4. 1/2
5. 1/3
6. 1/5
7. 1/4
8. 1/3
9. 1/2

P. 31
1. second pizza; thirds
2. first pizza; fourths
3. second pizza; halves

P. 32
Check students' work.

P. 33
Check students' work.

P. 34
Answers may vary.
1. square, cylinder, rectangle
2. cone, sphere, cylinder
3. cube, cone, cylinder, rectangle
4–6. Check students' drawings.

P. 35
Check students' drawings.
1. square
2. triangle
3. half sphere
4. triangle
5. triangle
6. 2 triangles

P. 36
1. more frogs
2. more turtles
3. 2 more
4. 4 more

P. 37
Students will fill in bar graph to show 8 cubes, 3 cones, 5 cylinders, 6 rectangular boxes

P. 38
1. +
2. –
3. –
4. +
5. +
6. –

P. 39
1. yes
2. quart jar
3. kitten
4. 90 degrees (middle thermometer)

Pp. 40–47
Students' responses will vary. Check work.